SIGN LANGUAGE AND
THE HEALTH CARE PROFESSIONAL

Ψ

Yasmin
Dela Vega

SIGN LANGUAGE AND
THE HEALTH CARE PROFESSIONAL

Debbie Cole

ROBERT E. KRIEGER PUBLISHING COMPANY
MALABAR, FLORIDA

Original Edition 1990

Printed and Published by
ROBERT E. KRIEGER PUBLISHING COMPANY, INC.
KRIEGER DRIVE
MALABAR, FL 32950

Printed in the United States of America.

Library of Congress Cataloging-in-Publication Data

Cole, Debbie L.
　　Sign language and the health care professional/by Debbie L.
　　Cole.—Original ed.
　　　　p. cm.
　　ISBN 0-89464-417-3 (alk. paper)
　　1. Deaf—Means of communication. 2. Sign language. 3. Medical
personnel and patient. 4. Interpersonal communicaiton. I. Title.
　　[DNLM: 1. Manual-Communication. 2. Physician-Patient Relations.
HV 2474 C689s]
HV2474.C65 1990
419'.02461—dc20
DNLM/DLC
for Library of Congress　　　　　　　　　　　　　　　89-20083
　　　　　　　　　　　　　　　　　　　　　　　　　　　　CIP

10　9　8　7　6　5

This book is dedicated to my parents,
Jim and Latriece Cross, in whose
shadow I grew to love and respect
deaf people. Their years of service
to the deaf in the Lord's church
inspired me to follow their example.
I am truly grateful for their love
and encouragement.

The author wishes to acknowledge the following people.

Deaf Consultants: Teresa B. Eckstein, Mary Pat Jones, Janet Saur and Yolanda Cabrera Villagran for their input, advice and support.

Fran Herrington-Borre for her suggestions and encouragement, especially in the early stages of the book.

My deaf friends whose confidence in my work, led me to write.

San Antonio interpreters for their support of the project.

Kip, Krystal and Valerie for allowing me to devote the time necessary to complete the work.

TABLE OF CONTENTS

FOREWORD

In her capacity as an interpreter, Debbie Cole found that when the health care professional and patient can establish even a minimal communication system, this helps establish or strengthen a bond of trust.

This booklet is an excellent reference for the health care professional who has a sincere interest in developing rapport with a patient whose main method of communication is the language of signs. The material is clear, concise enough to be useful to the busy health care professional, yet comprehensive enough to cover most topics about which the health care professional and patient need to communicate.

Debbie appropriately cautions the reader to use this information to facilitate basic care only. She cautions the reader always to rely on a professional interpreter to obtain medical histories, to provide instructions regarding medication or therapy, and to facilitate the exchange of technical or important information.

Happy signing!

Fran Herrington-Borre
Director
Austin Sign Language School

INTRODUCTION

This text is designed to facilitate the care of deaf and hearing impaired patients by health care professionals. Entering the hospital can be a frightening experience in itself, but when a person is faced with the problems of miscommunication, misunderstanding the procedures, or what is happening, the fear level is increased to a maximum. Imagine yourself entering a health care facility in a foreign country, where you don't know the language. Would you trust the medical professionals there? I believe it is safe to say that you would be, at the very least, concerned about the language barrier. You would be at the mercy of the judgment of strangers based on what they surmise the problem to be. Is it a wonder that a large number of deaf people believe they have been guinea pigs for health care in the past?

Section 504 of the Rehabilitation Act of 1973, 29 U.S.C. 79 provides that:

> . . . no otherwise qualified handicapped individual in the United States . . shall, solely by reason of his handicap, be excluded from participation in, be denied the benefits of, or be subjected to discrimination under any program or activity receiving Federal financial assistance.

This law includes Medicare and Medicaid payments made to the hospital for inpatient services to these patients. Equal access in this case means use of an interpreter and TTY (teletype phone device) availability. This ruling could not have come at a better time.

Since 1973 the National Center for Law and the Deaf has done an admirable job of disseminating information. The deaf population as a whole is now more aware of their rights.

After several chapters of basic information and signing techniques, the last chapter will focus on the role of interpreters. Briefly, the role of an interpreter is to assist the communication between the patient and the health care professional. Quality care begins with clear communication. The interpreter must be qualified to ensure the best level

1

of communication. The interpreter's purpose is to protect the health care facility as well as the patient. If the patient tells the interpreter he understands the risks and/or complications and signs papers to that effect, the hospital is protected in the case of a lawsuit. However, if there is no qualified interpreter present, having a patient sign papers is at best a liability risk. Someone who has taken a sign language course is **not a qualified** interpreter!

There are some myths about the deaf that need to be put to rest.

Myth 1. All Deaf read lips.

On the contrary, most deaf do not. You must realize these people have learned how to *nod appropriately* to save themselves from embarrassment and ridicule. According to Loraine Di Pietro in her booklet *How Deaf People Communicate*, "only 30% of English is visible on the lips." Many words look the same on the lips. It is even more difficult to read if the speaker is tight lipped or has a moustache.

Myth 2. Sign Language and English are the same.

As stated in *The Gallaudet Encyclopedia of Deaf People and Deafness Volume 3*, the two languages have completely different syntax, grammar and idiom vocabulary.

Myth 3. Notes can be used to explain.

The national reading level average among the deaf is fifth grade. *The Gallaudet Encyclopedia of Deaf People and Deafness Volume 2*, supports that fact. There are also a great many deaf who cannot read, because their parents shielded them at home until it was too late. Those who cannot read will tend to *nod appropriately* as well. So the chance of misunderstanding a written note is greater than one would think.

Myth 4. The family can sign or interpret.

Unfortunately, statistics show that 90% of hearing parents of deaf children never learn sign language. That information came from *An Orientation to Deafness for Social Workers* from Gallaudet University. If the family members can sign, it is inappropriate to ask them to interpret because of their emotional involvement in the case. It is also unethical for an interpreter who is a family member to do so.

Myth 5. Deaf people can't take care of a baby!

In our age of modern technology deaf people have many devices which utilize a lighting system to alert them to a baby's cry or the doorbell. Before these devices were invented, the deaf managed in other ways. A deaf woman once told me she placed the crib next to her bed and slept with her hand on the baby's buttocks so she could feel the baby stir when it awoke. Deaf mothers are not able to hear but there is no reason they cannot be just as attentive and loving with their babies as hearing mothers.

*Myth 6. If they have a hearing aid
they will understand me if I speak up.*

Amplification can help, but it also makes background noise louder and the message may not become clear. Many people have a tendency to talk louder if they notice a hearing aid. This may not improve understanding but can create embarrassment and confusion. The book *An Orientation to Deafness for Social Workers* from Gallaudet University states that this tendency can lead to rejection of the hearing aid and a refusal to use it.

*Myth 7. There are not that many deaf people
who use sign language.*

The book *Signing with Cindy* by Cindy Cochran states that "sign language is the third most used language in the United States."

This text will include only the basics to make your care of deaf easier, because the interpreter will not be available around the clock unless requested by the doctor in urgent situations. Nurses' sign communication should never be used when decisions are being made by the patient. Signed communications between patients and noncertified personnel should be limited to basic care. Let me stress that this book, even in conjunction with a sign language class, will in **no way** make you a qualified interpreter, so, for your own protection do not allow yourself to be put in that position. Hospitals and health care facilities across the country have been made aware of Section 504 rules and regulations. Lawsuits have already been heard and decided in favor of the deaf patient.

CHAPTER 1

MANUAL ALPHABET
AND CLASSIFIERS

Let's begin with the manual alphabet and some classifiers; they will lay the foundation on which you will develop your ability to communicate in sign language. I encourage you to pay special attention to the concepts in this lesson.

The American Manual Alphabet has been standardized and will appear the same across the nation as well as many other countries. Fingerspelling is a necessity for communication. All proper names of people, places, and medications will be fingerspelled. As a general rule American Sign Language (ASL) does not use a great deal of fingerspelling. However, to introduce yourself to another person it is necessary to spell out your name. Fingerspelling is not an easy task but it can be mastered with practice. There is a sign system which consists of fingerspelling only called the Rochester Method. The Rochester Method is not widely used so the knowledge of basic signs will be more beneficial.

There are some keys that will increase your ability to spell. First, hold your hand steady and let the fingers do the work. Second, practice making the letters blend one into the other. Remember clarity is more important than speed. Once you have learned the alphabet, let your fingers do the work, much the same as in typing. Concentrate on the word you are spelling, not on the letters themselves. Third, when reading fingerspelling, don't panic. Relax! You can catch the word if you are watching for syllables instead of letters. A fingerspelled word should be read the same as a written word on a page. There are tendencies of beginning signers that you should recognize. Don't look for the letters. The deaf will be blending them the same way as you do in your spelling. Sound the word out to yourself as you see it. If you are unsure of the word ask the person to spell it again. Don't ask the deaf to slow down. If they slow down you will see only letters and not the word. Another tendency is to focus on the hand that is spelling. It is best to observe the full body of the signer from the waist up as he signs and watch for clues on the mouth. Many deaf individuals will mouth part or all of the word as they spell it. If you watch only the hand, then the face, then refocus on the hand, the word will have already been spelled, and you will have missed it.

Practice spelling short three to five letter words to learn how to spell by blending letters as you build up speed. Slide your fingers from one letter into the other without a lot of opening and closing of the hand. Fingerspelling in front of a mirror will help you see the blends and aid your recognition of spelled words. Try to focus at a point between the face and the spelling hand to aid your reading of fingerspelling. This will center your attention on the hand for the words and the mouth for clues; notice body movement and placement with the peripheral vision. Try it, you will surprise yourself at the subtle movements you can observe peripherally with a little practice.

A classifier is a designated handshape used to show general items. Classifiers can be maneuvered or manipulated to specify spatial locations, mannerisms, movement, or placement of objects or people. The classifier used to illustrate an object or container can represent, for example, syrup poured over pancakes, or a baby's bottle of formula. Meaning depends on the way the hand is held and the movement of the handshape. The container classifier can also refer to shelves full of medicine vials or the kits the patient receives upon entering the hospital. The shape is an *open a*, open up the thumb and hold it on its side. The vehicle classifier can be used to represent any vehicle: boat, train, car, plane, bus, etc. It is, however, most often used to represent a car. It is a *3* hand lying on its side. The classifier for a person or large animal can be representative of a person walking up to another, or a bear lumbering through the forest. The context of the situation and sentence will give you the specifics needed to know who and or what the classifier is being used to illustrate. The person classifier can become a person staggering down the hall, or two people walking together. Parents may use this classifier for their child coming to them with a fever or in tears. The shape is a *1* (one) perpendicular to the floor.

The action person is one of the most widely used and is the basis for many ASL signs. It is a *v* held upside down, palm in. You can use it to

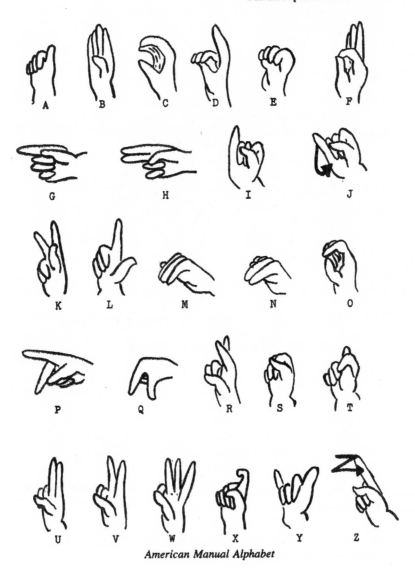

American Manual Alphabet

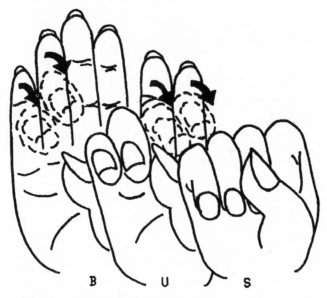

B   U   S

Illustration of a slide in fingerspelling

Commonly Spelled Words

bag	it	pen
bus	job	RN
cancer	kit	tape
do	lab	toe
hip	leg	tty
if	LVN	yes(for emphasis)

tell the patient to walk around a while or to lie down and rest. It can even indicate a person jumping up and down with excitement.

As you can see the classifiers are quite versatile and very important in one's communication with the deaf. Classifiers make it possible to put a great deal of information into a few signs or movements. There are two things to consider here. One is that the information needs to be condensed in this manner to help prevent eye strain as the eyes are muscles and do become tired. The other is that it is very easy to misconvey the message or information, without the skill of how to condense. For this reason one should not attempt to handle any situations requiring an interpreter for the patient's well being.

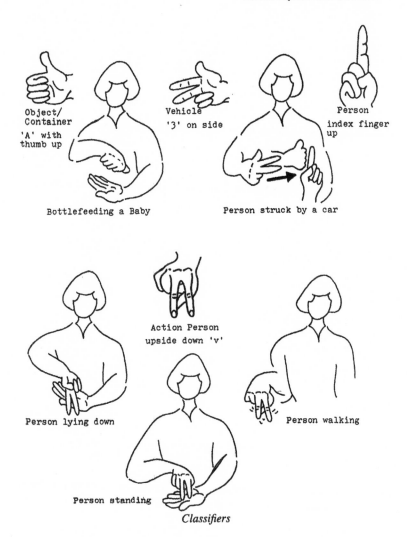

Object/
Container
'A' with
thumb up

Vehicle
'3' on side

Person
index finger
up

Bottlefeeding a Baby

Person struck by a car

Action Person
upside down 'v'

Person lying down

Person walking

Person standing

Classifiers

The classifiers give the signer the ability to communicate many things to a patient such as, to lie down, roll over on his side, or stand up and walk around, to name a few. Classifiers are unique to ASL which is universal among the deaf in America. It must be understood that while much information can be signed using classifiers with a minimum of movement or sign, all of the information is there in a condensed form. This system is easier on the eyes and creates less eye strain. It is also important to note that a great deal of deaf culture is tied to the language ASL and it is necessary to remember to accept the cultural differences without being critical.

CHAPTER 2

NUMBERS

This chapter will focus on numbers and counting. One of the beauties of sign language is that you can count to one billion on one hand. Numbers can be fun and easy if a little effort is expended to learn the technique. When counting one through five, the palm will face the signer. Six through ten will face outward, eleven through fifteen will face the signer, and sixteen and above will face outward. As a general rule, if you have only one number in a sentence, the hand will be held as stated above. It is important to note that when giving a string of numbers such as a phone number or zip code the palm will face out for all numbers. There will be a very slight pause between numbers to represent the dash in a phone number or social security number.

Some of the numbers will come naturally while others will have distinct differences from what you customarily use. For example, one and two are natural, three uses the thumb instead of the ring finger. This variation is to help differentiate between a *6* and a *3*. Six is made with the little finger on the tip of the thumb and the consecutive numbers follow with the ring finger on the thumb for seven, middle finger for eight and index finger for nine. Sometimes the finger will tap the thumb.

The twenties have some unique traits so each of them is illustrated. For twenties, use an *L* to represent the first two and then add the other number. For twenty, open and close the *L* up and down on the thumb to show a two and a zero. For twenty-one wiggle the index finger like the trigger finger on a gun or wiggle the thumb. All double numbers will bounce as in *22*. Make the number and bounce it over slightly to the right. Twenty-five is done by wiggling the middle and ring fingers up and down, or the little, middle and ring fingers wiggle. For the other twenties shape the *L* and then add or switch to the other number.

Thirty is a three curved into a zero repeatedly. Be sure to curve the fingers as they tap the thumb; otherwise, you will be saying *No* instead of *30*. Each of the numbers above thirty will follow the pattern of the first number first then the second digit.

For hundreds, curve the number into a loose *c* pulled toward you. The *c* will be made with the fingers used in making that number. It really takes the shape more of a claw hand for these numbers. One hundred is signed as *1,c*.

Deaf signers sometimes repeat numbers several times. For example with 31 you may see, 3-1-3-1-3-1. A common question is how to know which number is first? The hand will naturally make a slight turn of the wrist. For example, it will turn downward for 96 and upward for 69.

Along with numbers, it is important to learn the signs for weeks, months, years, and hours. To illustrate how many weeks, months, etc. are involved you will sign the number in conjunction with the sign. For a four-hour surgery, sign a *4* circling the clock face (palm of the other hand) clockwise. For a six weeks stay in the hospital, slide a *6* across the calendar (palm of the other hand).

As you can see, one hand will be moving. That is called the action hand. The other is stationary or a base hand. Many times the action hand will be the same as the signer's dominant hand, but it does not have to be so. It will be best to choose which hand will do the action and stay with it. Switching hands may bother deaf people and it can confuse the signer until the signs become natural or habit.

An ASL rules establishes that the past is behind you and the future is ahead. Therefore, to sign, *last week*, in one movement, you would slide a *1* across the calendar, turn palm in toward the body and throw it over your shoulder. *Next week* will extend out in front after it slides across. For past years up to four sign the number resting on top of an *s* near the shoulder of the dominant hand. Then wiggle the number back toward your shoulder. *Three years ago* will appear as a *3* wiggling back toward the shoulder resting on top of an *s*. Occasionally, you will see both hands, one on top of the other, wiggling the number.

Another ASL rule states that circling a sign means it is continuous. For example, "the patient was in surgery for hours!" *Hours* would be signed with the action hand index finger circling the clock face repeatedly. It follows then that sliding a *3* on the month sign repeatedly, in a circular motion could illustrate quarterly.

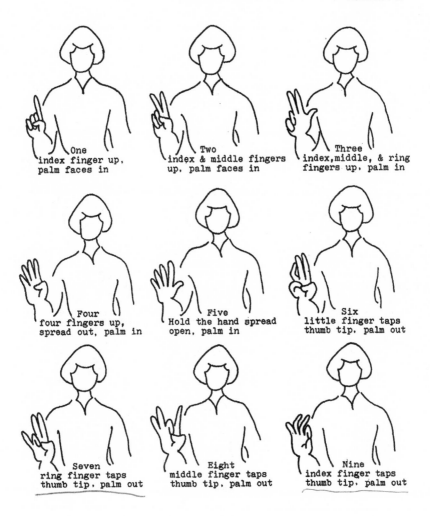

One
index finger up,
palm faces in

Two
index & middle fingers
up, palm faces in

Three
index, middle, & ring
fingers up, palm in

Four
four fingers up,
spread out, palm in

Five
Hold the hand spread
open, palm in

Six
little finger taps
thumb tip, palm out

Seven
ring finger taps
thumb tip, palm out

Eight
middle finger taps
thumb tip, palm out

Nine
index finger taps
thumb tip, palm out

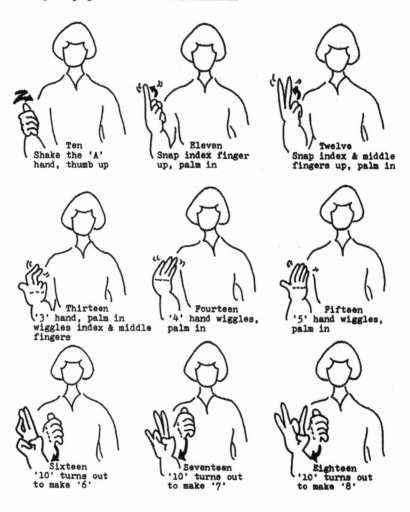

Ten
Shake the 'A'
hand, thumb up

Eleven
Snap index finger
up, palm in

Twelve
Snap index & middle
fingers up, palm in

Thirteen
'3' hand, palm in
wiggles index & middle
fingers

Fourteen
'4' hand wiggles,
palm in

Fifteen
'5' hand wiggles,
palm in

Sixteen
'10' turns out
to make '6'

Seventeen
'10' turns out
to make '7'

Eighteen
'10' turns out
to make '8'

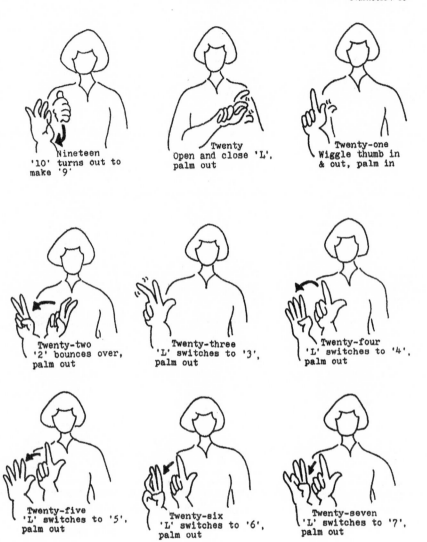

Nineteen
'10' turns out to
make '9'

Twenty
Open and close 'L',
palm out

Twenty-one
Wiggle thumb in
& out, palm in

Twenty-two
'2' bounces over,
palm out

Twenty-three
'L' switches to '3',
palm out

Twenty-four
'L' switches to '4',
palm out

Twenty-five
'L' switches to '5',
palm out

Twenty-six
'L' switches to '6',
palm out

Twenty-seven
'L' switches to '7',
palm out

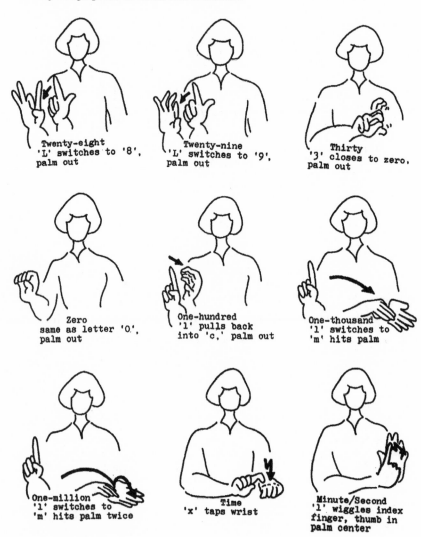

Twenty-eight
'L' switches to '8',
palm out

Twenty-nine
'L' switches to '9',
palm out

Thirty
'3' closes to zero,
palm out

Zero
same as letter 'O',
palm out

One-hundred
'1' pulls back
into 'c,' palm out

One-thousand
'1' switches to
'm' hits palm

One-million
'1' switches to
'm' hits palm twice

Time
'x' taps wrist

Minute/Second
'1' wiggles index
finger, thumb in
palm center

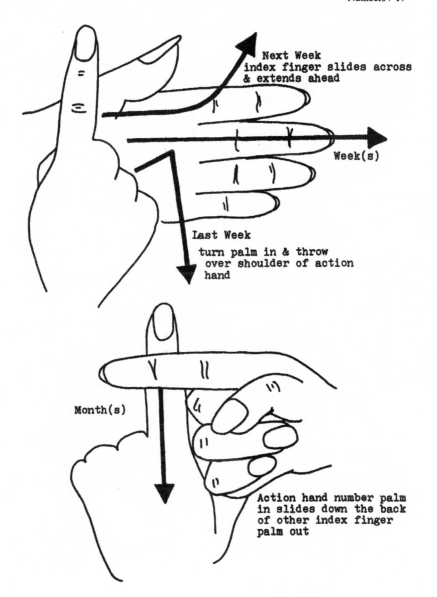

Next Week
index finger slides across
& extends ahead

Week(s)

Last Week
turn palm in & throw
over shoulder of action
hand

Month(s)

Action hand number palm
in slides down the back
of other index finger
palm out

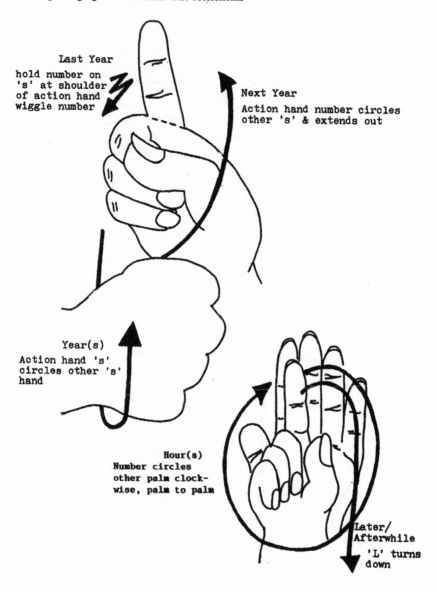

Last Year
hold number on
's' at shoulder
of action hand
wiggle number

Next Year
Action hand number circles
other 's' & extends out

Year(s)
Action hand 's'
circles other 's'
hand

Hour(s)
Number circles
other palm clock-
wise, palm to palm

**Later/
Afterwhile**
'L' turns
down

CHAPTER 3

TIME REFERENCE

As stated in Chapter 2, the past is always behind the signer and the future will stretch or reach ahead. This chapter will give you the basic time reference signs seen in ASL. One of the grammatical rules of ASL requires the time reference to appear first in a story or sentence. Be careful to watch for the time reference because ASL uses root words. There are no prefixes or suffixes in ASL. The time reference sign will give you the tense in context.

When signing phrases such as *morning, noon, and night* or *three times a day*, the base hand symbolizes the horizon line while the action hand represents the sun coming up, straight up at noon, and going down in the evening. Occasionally, if there is a specific time for medication you will see a number in conjunction with the morning sign and or evening sign depending on the patient's schedule for medication.

Yesterday may appear as an *a* or *y*. Both are acceptable in ASL. To sign a particular day of the week, form the letter and move it in the air in a circular motion. Two exceptions are *Thursday* which is made with a *t* bouncing to an *h* twice, and *Sunday* which taps the church doors in a downward motion. The hand may face in or out for days of the week. When the situation occurs regularly such as every Monday the *m* is pulled down. To sign a day last week sign past and the day. For a day in the future extend the action hand forward and then sign the day.

Time references are important; without them one would have no concept of the time frame. The context could be changed tremendously without the proper time reference.

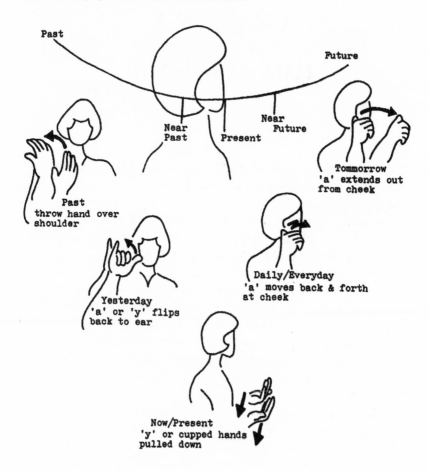

Past

Future

Near Past

Present

Near Future

Past
throw hand over
shoulder

Tommorrow
'a' extends out
from cheek

Daily/Everyday
'a' moves back & forth
at cheek

Yesterday
'a' or 'y' flips
back to ear

Now/Present
'y' or cupped hands
pulled down

Day(s)
one or another number
comes across to the
elbow

Morning
'5' comes up to the
body on the outside
of the other arm

Afternoon
'5' goes down away
from the body, over
the other arm

Three times a day/Morning,Noon & Night
'5' hand extends out to the side,
straight up at the shoulder & down
across the other arm

Immediate/Stat
'L' strikes and repels
other palm

Twice a day/Morning & Night (Evening)
'5' hand extends out to the side &
down across the other arm

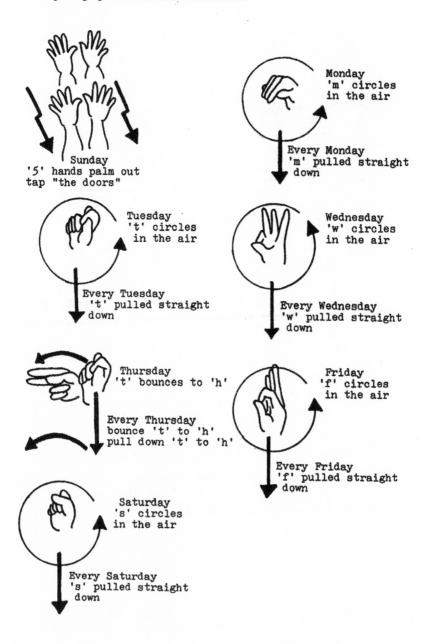

Sunday
'5' hands palm out
tap "the doors"

Monday
'm' circles
in the air

Every Monday
'm' pulled straight
down

Tuesday
't' circles
in the air

Every Tuesday
't' pulled straight
down

Wednesday
'w' circles
in the air

Every Wednesday
'w' pulled straight
down

Thursday
't' bounces to 'h'

Every Thursday
bounce 't' to 'h'
pull down 't' to 'h'

Friday
'f' circles
in the air

Every Friday
'f' pulled straight
down

Saturday
's' circles
in the air

Every Saturday
's' pulled straight
down

CHAPTER 4

PERSONNEL

This chapter will deal with the signs used to designate different people and or their occupation. To distinguish the sign as a person, a second movement will be necessary as illustrated in *interpret/interpreter*. You will notice that the sign represents both the verb and the noun. This custom is standard with the American Sign Language (ASL). Verbs are directional in many cases. To tell a patient that you will give him medication, *give* will be signed toward the patient-recipient.

Pronouns must clearly designate the referenced persons. Pronouns may be vague in the English language creating confusion because they are abstract. Deaf people in general have some difficulty with communication about abstract thought or ideas; it is controlled by the same center in the brain as hearing and gets limited stimulation. In hearing culture we were raised to believe it is rude to point. In deaf culture and in ASL it is a must to point to the person to whom you are referring. If a deaf woman is referring to something she and her husband have agreed upon, she will point to him and herself even if the husband is not in the room. She will sign his name and point to a space beside her that will represent the husband. Anytime there are two pronouns in an ASL sentence, the first is the direct object and the second is the subject.

For better understanding the deaf tend to point out or refer to outstanding characteristics. If two doctors are working together on a case one may be named as the bald doctor and the other as the one with a beard or maybe with glasses. It must be understood that this practice is not derogatory but is simply a means of identifying a specific person in clear concrete terms. Don't be offended if a deaf individual tells you to slim down or to shave a beard. Such comments are because of genuine concern for you and are not intended as insults. If there is any doubt, you can see this by their facial expression. ASL tends to be straightforward and to the point, to leave no room for error. Some might think the deaf are rude in this aspect, but this is not the case. Deaf culture deals in black and white and does not have the inhibitions of the hearing culture. We would never ask someone their rate of pay. However, this is a normal part of deaf culture in daily life. If you plan to cross the cultures you must be accepting and understanding of the differences.

In ASL the words *I* and *me* are signed in the same manner. Point to yourself, in the center of the chest, to sign *me*. To sign *you* point to the person to whom you are speaking.

To designate a person drop 5 hands perpendicular to the floor this illustrates the form of the person. The signs for people will either begin at the forehead or chin in many cases. The rule states above the nose is masculine and below the nose is feminine. Growing up in the deaf community I was told the reason for this was the men did the thinking and the women did the talking. In recent years, I had a sign class student with another viewpoint. She said, "It's because the women tell the men what to think." Which ever way you choose to remember it, be sure to make the distinction in your signs.

Interpreter/Interpret
'f' hands twist up &
down, drop '5' hands
downward for person

Doctor
take the pulse with
'd' or 'm' hand

Nurse
take the pulse with
'n' hand

Psychology/Psychologist
'5' taps between thumb &
fingers   palms face each
other, add '5's down for
person

Operation/Surgeon/Surgery
'a' makes an 'incision' on
other palm, add '5's down
for person

Patient
'p' makes a cross
on the shoulder

Technique/Technician
middle finger of action
hand taps side of other
hand, add '5's for
person

Help/Aide
'a' hand in palm of
other hand upward
motion, add '5's for
person

Special/Specialist
action hand pulls index
up, add '5's for person

Family
'f' hands circle out
away from the body,
as in a family around
the dinner table

Friend
'1' hands interlock
& then flip to inter-
lock again

Boy/Male
'5' hand closes
to 'grab the bill
of the cap'

Girl/Female
'a' strokes the cheek
to 'grab the bonnet
strings'

Man
'5' taps forehead with
thumb & drops to center
of chest

Woman
'5' taps chin with
thumb & drops to
center of chest

Mother/Mom/Mommy
'5' taps chin with
thumb

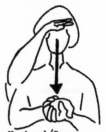

Father/Dad/Daddy
'5' taps forehead
with thumb

Husband/Groom
Boy down to clasped
hands (marry)

Bride/Wife
cupped '5' hand
down to clasped
hands (marry)

Child/Children
'5' hand taps the
heads of children

Baby/Infant
arms folded naturally
to cradle a baby

We/Us
index finger taps
chest from one side
to the other

My/Mine
'5' hand flat on
chest

**Your/Yours
Their/Theirs**
extend five hand
toward person(s)

Daughter- girl + baby

Son- boy + baby

Name
'h' action hand taps
top of 'h' base hand

CHAPTER 5

THE BASICS

This chapter will give you a well rounded collection of verbs and nouns for conversation and some common responses to questions.

When asking a question requiring a yes or no answer, lean toward the patient slightly and raise your eyebrows. If asking a who, what, where, when, how or why question tilt your head back a little and squint or furrow your forehead. These are visual cues to the response needed. A common mistake is to ask where a patient lives but the face asks for a yes or no answer. Deaf people will tend to watch the face more closely than the sign, so the visual cues are part of the question.

In discussing facial expression it must be noted that the deaf are experts in reading our eyes and faces. It is almost impossible to hide or cover our feelings when they show on the face. So please do not make the mistake of saying one thing and meaning another. If you seem apprehensive about something it will be noticed. Maybe you have been instructed to insert an ENG tube on a deaf patient but you don't feel comfortable in doing so. They will see that in your face. I must warn you that smiling too much can also have an unnerving effect. As stated in the introduction most hearing parents of deaf do not have a native language with their children. That fact helps to perpetuate the paranoia of the culture. I'm sure we all at sometime or another in our lives have felt as though other people were talking about us. Without being able to hear and communicate easily with those about us, the tendency is to assume the worst.

Leaving the room of a deaf patient without telling him where you are going is an insult. In deaf culture one always states why he is leaving before he does so. Otherwise, he will offend the people involved. It is understandable that because you are caring for other patients you will need to enter and leave the room several times. Just imagine if you are the patient and the nurse comes in to check your vitals and then races out to the call of an emergency for another patient. Because you did not hear the alarm, you may assume you are the emergency or that something is wrong.

Along the same lines, if you take a patient's possession to save or put away, make sure he knows what you are doing. Some deaf people have mistakenly assumed the item was being stolen simply because they didn't understand it was being stored for safe keeping. Once when visiting a deaf friend in the hospital, the nurse asked why the patient had not eaten the previous meal. The patient answered in sign, "I didn't have my teeth; the other nurse took them."

It is important to tell your deaf patient what you are doing. Many times a deaf person is poked and prodded without explanation simply because the nurse is unable to communicate. Be sensitive to the deaf patient's needs and feelings.

In caring for deaf patients it is necessary to understand how they feel about eyes and hands. The eyes serve as both the eyes and ears so consequently eye surgery for a deaf person can be very traumatic. The thought of losing one's eyesight creates greater stress because it could mean total isolation. It is true that there are touch sign systems but learning them would require major adjustments and changes in life-style.

The hands are the cherished voice of the deaf. It is a person's ability to sign that gains acceptance in the deaf community. When trying to get your attention, a deaf person will wave his hand at you. If there is no response he may flail his hands in the air or slap the bed or table. This action is the equivalent of raising your voice or even shouting to get someone to listen. A deaf patient in recovery after surgery flailing his hands may be viewed as thrashing or even combative. Many times he only wants to communicate. Sadly, the medical team unaware of this desire or need, will restrain the patient. This action only serves to create more anxiety. Tying down a deaf person's hands is like having your mouth taped shut. You have no way to communicate and are at the mercy of others.

It should be noted that sometimes a deaf person will shake his head and sign *no* when he does not understand. A deaf woman went to the dentist to have a tooth extracted. The dentist assuming she could read lips, asked if she wanted novocaine. The woman, not understanding, shook her head no. To her horror the dentist pulled the woman's tooth without any medication.

In signing *here* hold the hands closer together, and let them make wider movements in signing *where*. Sign *please* using one hand, but *enjoy, appreciate,* and *pleasure* may be signed with both hands. There are two signs in this lesson which require special care. The sign *want* and *hungry* can both mean lust when signed several times, especially if the facial expression fits.

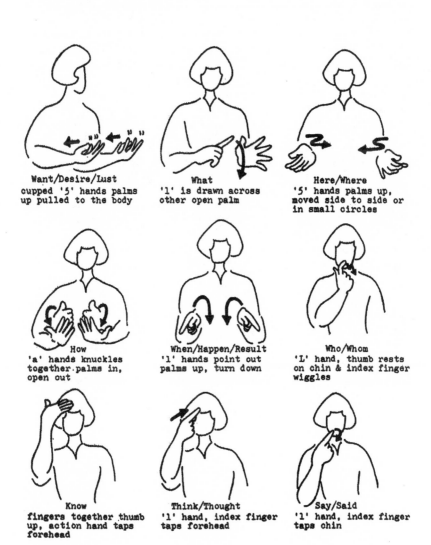

Want/Desire/Lust
cupped '5' hands palms
up pulled to the body

What
'1' is drawn across
other open palm

Here/Where
'5' hands palms up,
moved side to side or
in small circles

How
'a' hands knuckles
together.palms in,
open out

When/Happen/Result
'1' hands point out
palms up, turn down

Who/Whom
'L' hand, thumb rests
on chin & index finger
wiggles

Know
fingers together thumb
up, action hand taps
forehead

Think/Thought
'1' hand, index finger
taps forehead

Say/Said
'1' hand, index finger
taps chin

Tell

'1' hand, index finger
under the chin points
out

Ask/Query/Question

'1' hand drops to 'x'
to form a '?' in the air

Please/Enjoy/Pleasure
Appreciate
'5' hand circles chest
clockwise

Sorry/Regret/Apologize
'a' hand circles chest
clockwise

Good/Thank-you
'5' hand touches lips
& extends out

Yes/Positive/Affirmative
's' hand nods up &
down

No/Negative
index & middle fingers
close down to thumb

Can/Able/Possible/Capable
's' hands drop down

Can't
'1' hands, index
finger strikes the
other index finger

Will/Shall
'5' hand palm faces
cheek extends out
from the ear

Won't/Refuse
'a' hand palm faces
cheek thrown over
shoulder

Come
person classifiers
pulled to the body

Go
person classifiers
extend out from the
body

Stay
'y' hand drops down
firmly

Wait/Delay
'5' hands palms up
all fingers wiggle

Lipread/Oral/Speech
crooked 'v' hand circles
mouth

Note/Write
fist with index finger
on tip of thumb 'writes'
in other palm

Thirsty
'1' hand, index
finger slides down
throat

Hungry/Wish
'c' hand traces
the esophagus once

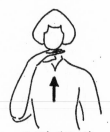

Full(of food)
'4' hand pulled up
under the chin

Eat/Food
closed hand finger
tips on thumb, taps
the lips

Drink
'c' hand lifts 'cup'
up to the mouth

Milk/Formula
's' hand opens & closes
as in milking a cow

Tea
'f' hand swirls 'tea
bag' in 'c' hand

Coffee
's' hand circles counter
clockwise on top of 's'
as grinding coffee

Coke
'L' hand, index finger
touches shoulder &
thumb wiggles

Apple
'x' hand twists on
cheek

CHAPTER 6

ANATOMY

The signs used for anatomy are natural so they should come easily. Basically, one only needs to point to the part of the body in question. Internal organs will be fingerspelled with classifier illustrations. More classifiers exist than were discussed and illustrated in Chapter 1. For this reason, coupled with the fact that the patient may not be familiar with the internal organs of the body, an interpreter would have to be present. Only the signs and classifiers necessary to care for the patient in the hospital are included, not the signs to explain or diagnose the condition. Just as it would be unwise to send a level one nursing student to ICU without supervision, it is unwise to attempt to interpret in situations requiring experience and ASL language expertise.

Recently, a job fair for health care professionals was held at St. Philip's College in San Antonio. Each of the various hospital representatives from around the state was systematically asked if he had a staff interpreter for deaf patients. Not one of the hospitals represented had an in-house interpreter. One representative indicated some of the nurses had taken a sign language course and could communicate. When asked if they were ceritifed she smiled and stated, "Well, there is a service we can call to get one if we have to." It is not a choice; interpreter service is required by law. It is impossible to learn a language in six weeks or even a semester. That is why foreign languages are always taught in various levels and the students realize their weakness in fluency and understanding. It takes time. ASL must be given the same respect. One can study and work with deaf people for years and not learn everything that may occur in various situations. You must know your limitations and act accordingly.

Given the basics outlined in this book, you will be able to tell the deaf patient what you are doing, i.e., to give an injection, take blood pressure, or give an enema. Your basic sign knowledge will show the patient you care enough to try to communicate. Your patients will appreciate your efforts and will feel more comfortable in your care. You should avoid getting into situations beyond your abilities. Examples of such situations are listed in Chapter 12.

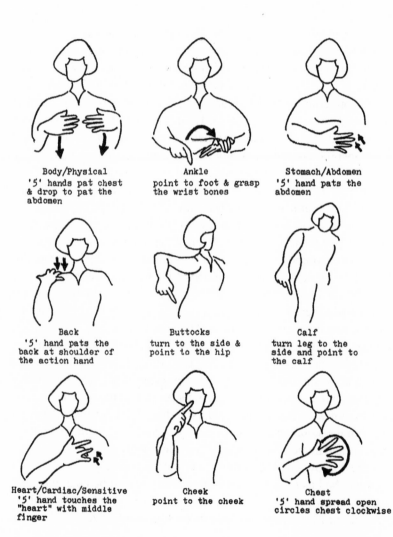

Body/Physical
'5' hands pat chest & drop to pat the abdomen

Ankle
point to foot & grasp the wrist bones

Stomach/Abdomen
'5' hand pats the abdomen

Back
'5' hand pats the back at shoulder of the action hand

Buttocks
turn to the side & point to the hip

Calf
turn leg to the side and point to the calf

Heart/Cardiac/Sensitive
'5' hand touches the "heart" with middle finger

Cheek
point to the cheek

Chest
'5' hand spread open circles chest clockwise

Ear/Hear
point to ear with
index finger

Elbow
action hand cups
the other elbow

Head
'5' hand fingers
together bent, taps
head top and base

Brain/Mind
tap side of forehead
with bent index finger

Leg
stroke thigh up
& down

Foot/Feet
point to each foot

Hand
stroke base hand with
action hand

Arm
run the index finger
down the arm

Eye
point to the eye(s)

Mouth/Lips
circle the mouth with
index finger

Tongue
touch the tongue

Teeth/Dentist
tap the teeth with
index finger

Shoulder
'5' hand pats other
shoulder

Breast
'5' hand fingers to-
gether cup each
breast

Anus/Rectum
'o' or 'f' hand changes
to 'l' and points to
rectum

Face
'l' hand circles
the face

CHAPTER 7

HYGIENE

This chapter shows the signs that will be helpful in caring for the patient's needs. Many of these signs are natural and will be easy to learn. You will notice again that several of the signs have more than one meaning. Distinguishing which meaning is intended is a little more difficult. Various facial expressions and body movements will aid your comprehension of what is said. For example, if signing *paralyzed* the shoulders will tense up and the face will be tight. If signing *frozen* the body will shiver and the mouth will pucker. Sometimes the sign will be made identical but the facial expression will explain the context or change the meaning. ASL uses the speed and method of movement of the sign for adjectives and adverbs. The movement will also indicate the speaker's tone and mood. An emphatic movement shows the intensity of the feeling or situation. The sign *wet* and the sign *humid* will appear different even though they are the same sign. *Humid* will use more fingertip movement and *wet* will utilize the whole hand. The facial expressions will of course be different as well.

If you receive a response of a blank face or head nod for every question, chances are you are not being understood. The patient may be nodding in self-defense. Remember there are many deaf who cannot read or read lips, so to cover up this fact they will sometimes nod yes to everything.

A deaf man went into the hospital for surgery. The hospital had agreed to call for an interpreter, however, the call was not made. An interpreter had gone to sit with the family after the surgery had begun. She answered the call when the doctor phoned the waiting room because the family was also deaf. The doctor seemed pleased an interpreter was there and said the recovery nurses would send for the interpreter as soon as the patient was settled. They waited but no call came. Finally, the family became impatient and asked at the information desk. The information clerk called recovery, whereupon the nurses assured her an interpreter was not needed as the patient could understand everything. The patient did not read or read lips. The family insisted the interpreter go into recovery with the patient. Sadly, the family was forced to mention that the law required an interpreter be present and legal action could result if no interpreter was permitted. The head of recovery sent for the interpreter. The head nurse met the interpreter at the door and wanted to know about that law. Being well prepared the interpreter was able to show her what she needed. The nurse in charge of the patient told the interpreter she could interpret all she wanted, but the patient was ready to go up to his room. Upon seeing the interpreter the patient immediately told her his leg was numb. As she began speaking for the patient the nurse whirled around to find out the interpreter's problem. The patient repeated the problem through the interpreter. The nurse decided to verify the information. After seeing it was true she decided to keep the patient in recovery a while longer. The doctor came in to check on the patient saying he was glad to have an interpreter because it was certainly easier than writing notes. The nurse stated, "the patient reads lips," which the interpreter signed to the patient. The patient in shock replied, "NO, I do not!" The nurse in defense said he had been nodding to all her questions. When the doctor asked if the patient was ready to go up to the room, the nurse was able to say, "Not yet his leg is still numb." The nurse knew an interpreter had enabled her to know the patient's condition and that was enough.

As interpreters we are present to facilitate the care of the deaf patient by assisting communication between doctor and patient. Interpreters do not want to usurp the authority or question the ability of health care professionals looking after patients. After all **you**, the caregiver, are the trained medical professionals. Interpreters can provide the clear communication necessary with the patient to insure their best care. Obviously working with a deaf patient can take more time if you are forced to write notes or try to mime what you need to communicate. Using an interpreter can cut the time in half. In fact, anytime decisions must be made by the patient or precise communication is critical, an interpreter is required by law.

In/Into/Involved
closed hand fingertips
to thumb insert into
'c' hand

Out/Outside
Pull action hand out
of 'c' hand, close the
hand as you draw it out

Put
closed hands fingertips
to thumbs move from one
place to another

Take
'5' hand moves to
grab 'object' in
the air

Give/Offer/Suggest
closed hands fingertips
to thumbs, palms up
move toward the receiver

Sit/Chair
'action person' sits
on 'h' palms down

Wheelchair
'1' hands palms facing
in circle out from the
body

Bed
Lay the head over on
'5' hand

Pillow
Lay the head over on
'5' hands, palms to-
gether

Crutch
Hold hands as if
gripping crutches
move hands forward

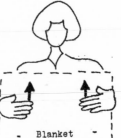

Blanket
'5' hands palms in
slide up the body as a
blanket

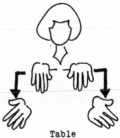

Table
'5' hands palms down
draw top and sides
of a square

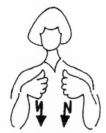

Bath/Bathe/Wash
'a' hands palms in
slide up and down as
rubbing soap on the
body

Dress/Clothes
'5' hands palms in
move up and down as
in throwing on clothes

Soap
5' hand picks up the
'soap' bar from the
other hand

Hot/Heat
'claw' hand opens as
it turns out "to spew
out hot coffee"

Cold/Winter
's' hands shiver at
sides

Warm/Friendly
's' opens to '5' as
"blow on the hand to
warm it"

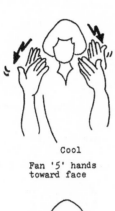

Cool

Fan '5' hands
toward face

Frozen/Paralyzed

'5' hands pull up
into claw position

Shower

Closed hand, opens
to '5' over head to
"spray"

Water
'w' taps the mouth
index finger to lips

Dry/Dull
'x' pulled across
base of the chin

Wet/Damp/Humid/Moist
'5' hands open and
close downward or rub
fingertips to thumb

Comb
'claw' hand strokes
hair

Brush
'a' hand strokes
hair

Raise/High/Up
lift '5' hand palm up

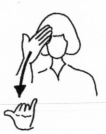

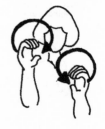

Low
lower '5' hand

Why
touch forehead with
'5' drop to a 'y'

Finish/Done/Stop it/
No more/past tense
flip '5' hands outward

Patient/Endure/Suffer
'a' hand, thumb against
lips, slides down to
chin

Elevator
'e' hand moves up
and down

Test/Screen/Examine
'c' hands circle the
face in an alternating
pattern

Numb
'5' hand middle finger
strokes chest upward (feel),
'o' hand is thrust out from
body (none)

These are the types of communications which would be appropriate for a beginning signer to have with the deaf patients. Notice the difference between the English and ASL version of the sentences.

Practice Sentences

English	ASL glosses
1. Put your clothes in the closet.	Clothes put closet.
2. Do you want a blanket?	Blanket want you?
3. You can go out in a wheel chair.	Out can wheel chair.
4. You can walk on crutches.	Walk can crutches.
5. I want a pillow.	Pillow want me.
6. I will give you a bath.	Me will (or help) bath you.
7. Here is the soap.	Soap here.
8. Do you want a shower?	Shower want you?
9. It is cool outside.	Outside cool, cool.
10. Do you want a hot bath?	Bath hot want you?
11. Don't get your stiches wet.	Stiches wet can't, can't.
12. Put your clothes on the table.	Clothes your put table.
13. Please, lower the bed.	Bed low please.
14. The brush is on the table.	Brush where table.
15. Do you feel stiff?	You stiff you?
16. The water is warm.	Water warm.
17. Are you cold?	Cold you?
18. Please, raise the bed.	Bed raise please.
19. You can sit up today.	Now day sit can.
20. I'm going to take out the I.V.	I.V. take out me.

Sign #20 gently please or the patient will be afraid it will be painful!

CHAPTER 8

LABOR AND DELIVERY

This chapter has a variety of signs but the majority will concern labor and delivery. This is a good opportunity to warn you that it may take from thirty minutes to two hours to bring in an interpreter. The average elapsed time is an hour. There are emergency pager systems in use in Deaf Councils and Interpreter Services. Unfortunately, getting the call made from the hospital may take some time. Often interpreters must give the same hospital the phone number and pager number again and again because it is "not in the records." Compounding the problem of getting an interpreter quickly is the fact that the police departments, courts, etc. are pulling from the same pool of interpreters.

More and more deaf fathers, like hearing fathers, are seizing the opportunity to enter the delivery room. This can create special challenges in delivery. Both the mother and father should be able to communicate with the doctor in such cases. Interpreters are becoming standard procedure in many situations.

A patient entering the hospital for surgery, upon admittance answered the medical history questions. The next day, the patient in pre-op was asked by the anesthesiologist, double checking, if he had any allergies. The patient gave a different answer. The question was signed more clearly. This time the patient said, "Yes, almost die." and spelled the name of the medication. The anesthesiologist was grateful for the interpreter because he had intended to use that very medication. Working together, doctor and interpreter, minimized the patient's risk.

This lesson has two signs that call for special care and attention. Diabetes is sometimes signed as sugar. However, some deaf have no knowledge or understanding of the disease, so they could only interpret it as sugar. It is best to sign it as *sugar, sick*, which depending on their experiences, still may not be clearly understood. Another sign with a similar problem is allergy. Unless the patient understands what an allergy is, again, he may misunderstand the sign. Likely you may find patients who are allergic to various medications but don't realize it. Maybe the patient's parents did all the talking with the doctor at the time the patient suffered from the allergy or the doctor didn't have an interpreter to explain an allergic reaction.

Smoke
'v' hand held at the lips as in holding a cigarette

Addict/Drug Habit
'a' hand hits the crook of arm with the base of the 'a'

Cocaine
thumb of 'a' hand presses the base of each nostril

Drunk/Alcoholic
'y' hand, palm out slumps down across face

Alcohol/Liquor/Whiskey
hands held with index & little fingers extended, one taps the top of the other

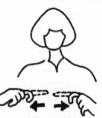

Allergy/Enemy
'1' hands, palms down pull apart & close to 'x's'

Diabetes/Sugar/Sweet
'5' hand wipes chin & becomes an 'a'

Cry/Weep/Tears
'1' hands, index fingers draw tears down the cheeks

Sad
'5' hands pulled down in front of face, drop head

Happy/Glad
'5' hands stroke
chest in upward
circular motion

Mad/Angry
Claw hand(s) move
up from abdomen with
force

Die/Death/Dead
'5' hands, action hand
palm down & base hand
palm up flip over

Live/Life/Address
'a' hands slide up
the body

Heal/Cure/Healthy/Well
'5' hands grasp shoulder
as they pull up into 's'

Cough
's' hand hits the
chest forcefully

Cold/Tissue/Kleenex
grab the nose with
thumb & index finger
in short down strokes

Afraid/Scared/Fear
's' hands spread to '5'
across the body with a
shudder

Shock
index finger of '1'
taps forehead and '5'
hands drop palm down

Crippled/Lame
'l' hands, palms
down "walk with a
limp" up & down

Nervous/Shaky
'5' hands, palms face
in to each other, &
shake

Problem/Difficulty
'v' hands with v's
crooked, palms in,
strike each other as
they move up & down

See/Look/Watch
'v' hand palm in
turns out as it
extends from the eye

Eye Glasses
'L' hands bent to
encircle the eyes

Take Care Of
'v' action hand on
top of 'v' moves
counter clockwise

Pregnant/Expecting
'5' hands extend to
encircle the stomach
& interlock fingers

Birth/Deliver
base hand palm up &
action hand palm up
drops out of base hand

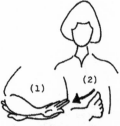

Cesarean Section
Sign baby and then
draw an 'a' across
the "incision"

Labor/Crowning
clasp 's' hand with
base hand & press 's'
outward, puff cheeks

Menstruate/Period
'a' hand taps cheek
with knuckles

Weigh/Pounds
'h' hands, action
hand rocks atop the
other

Big/Length
stretch '5' hands apart
to show size

Vagina
'L' hands touch
to form triangle

Penis
's' base hand, '1'
action hand shakes
index finger

Circumcision
'a' hands, action
hand thumb circles
other thumb & up

Intercourse
'v' hands, action
hand taps the other
thumbs together

Breastfeed/Nurse
open & close '5'
hand over breast

CHAPTER 9

VITAL SIGNS

These signs will probably be the most useful to you in the care of your deaf patients. As you can see, several of them require the use of two or more signs to illustrate the meaning of one word. Without the combination of signs, one stands a greater chance of being misunderstood, which occurs frequently. *Recovery room*, for example needs a combination of five signs to be clear. They are: *surgery, finish, heal, room, wake-up*.

The sign for *hurt* or *pain* is in this chapter. It is difficult to describe accurately whether pain is sharp, radiating, hot, dull, etc. A story that circulated in the 1980s helps support this concept. Once a deaf person went to a hospital complaining of abdominal pain. No interpreter was called, but that patient was subjected to three surgical procedures. The patient was still suffering from the original complaint and was undernourished. The medical team decided to do a subclavian line. The floor nurse suggested to the family they demand an interpreter because the face would be covered. (This is a simple procedure, however, covering the face of a deaf person who is awake can create undue anxiety. He may start *thrashing* because he doesn't know what is happening. **Restraint will only increase the stress.**) The nurse was reprimanded by the doctors, but her initiative may have saved the hospital a lawsuit. Up until that moment everything done to that patient was illegal by Section 504 and in direct violation of the patient's rights. Now, for the first time since entering the hospital, the patient had each of the three operations explained through an interpreter. Finally the patient was able to give the doctors a clear picture of where the pain originated and to describe other symptoms. Acting on the new information, the client underwent yet another surgery, a cystectomy. This time the treatment was a success and the patient could begin to heal. The doctors in this case had written notes, but to no avail. When asked where is the pain, the patient may point to several different areas or an entire region. In that situation, the health care professional can only assume what is wrong without an interpreter to query the patient for verification. Don't make this mistake! It could cost your license and your ability to practice medicine.

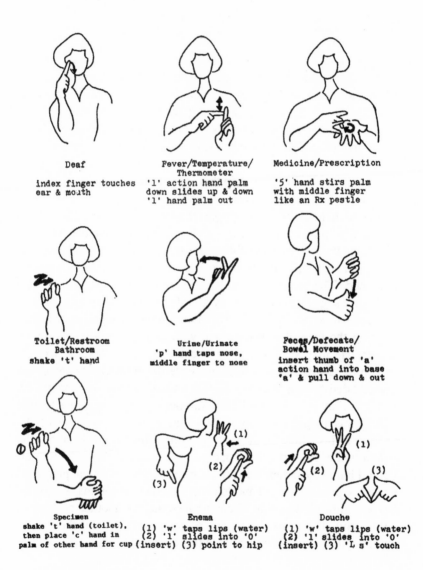

Deaf	**Fever/Temperature/ Thermometer**	**Medicine/Prescription**
index finger touches ear & mouth	'1' action hand palm down slides up & down '1' hand palm out	'5' hand stirs palm with middle finger like an Rx pestle

Toilet/Restroom Bathroom	**Urine/Urinate**	**Feces/Defecate/ Bowel Movement**
shake 't' hand	'p' hand taps nose, middle finger to nose	insert thumb of 'a' action hand into base 'a' & pull down & out

Specimen	**Enema**	**Douche**
shake 't' hand (toilet), then place 'c' hand in palm of other hand for cup	(1) 'w' taps lips (water) (2) '1' slides into '0' (insert) (3) point to hip	(1) 'w' taps lips (water) (2) '1' slides into '0' (insert) (3) 'L s' touch

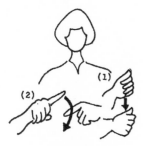

Constipated
(1) 'a' is pulled down &
out of base of 'a', (2)
strike index finger with
the other

Diarrhea
'5' pulled down &
out of base of 'a'

Pill/Capsule
'g' hand opens to
'1' to "pop pill
in mouth, open mouth

Liquid
'a' hand palm out "pours"
into 'c' hand

Blood Pressure
'5' hand opens &
closes on arm

Injection/Shot
'3' hand, fingers &
thumb close to "inject"

Hurt/Pain
'1' hands twist & press
together

Enter/Admit
'5' hand slides under
'5' palms down

Excuse/Discharge/Release
'5' hand slides off
palm of '5' hand

Examine/Palpate
'5' hands fingers to-
gether, bent thump or
press over chest area

Emergency
shake an 'e' hand

TTY call
tip of 'x' slides
down the index finger
of 'l' hand

Ambulance
'5' hands twist,
puff cheeks

Phone/Call
'y' hand held to
ear as receiver

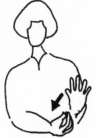

Draw Blood
'5' hand at crook of
elbow pulls out to close

Gas
's' hand opens to '5'
at elbow, thrust out

CHAPTER 10

SYMPTOMS

The signs in this chapter will illustrate the various symptoms experienced. Again several meanings are attached to one sign. Watch for facial expression to indicate the proper meaning in context. To sign *smell* or *odor* the signer's face should have a frown to show the distaste. If the smell is pleasant, such as a fragrance, the face would illustrate the appreciation for the smell.

I felt it would now be a good time to give you an example of how the deaf would describe symptoms in ASL. If you find this information difficult to understand, you are not alone. The complexity and importance of the information are the very reason for using a qualified professional interpreter.

ASL: Baseball play me. Hurt how? Hit, fall down blood. Happen broke knee me. Doctor see finish here. Knee worse hurt hurt!! Bone ugly whew!! Hurt worse. Now fix help me please. Doctor query do do pain me?

English: I was playing baseball. I got hit and fell down and my knee started bleeding. It is broken. I am here to see the doctor. It really hurts and it looks awful. I can see the bone and the pain is getting worse. Please take care of it now. I want to know what to do about the pain. Tell the doctor I need to know.

See the difference between the ASL and the English descriptions of a compound fracture of the knee. In ASL you will be given the events leading up to the situation. The sentence will follow the sequence in which things occurred. The syntax for ASL is time, topic, verb, adjective, adverb, direct object and subject. ASL is not English and will not follow English word order or English grammatical structure, whether it is signed or written. ASL will omit articles and prepositions as we know them. When something is under the bed, it would be signed as *shoes, bed (point under)*. All the information is there in a minimum of movement or sign. ASL takes into consideration that the eyes are muscles and will need short respite from time to time. When it is accepted that ASL is a language in its own right, we will not need to question why it is so different from English. To help clarify, let me give you some additional information on the syntax. Time is given first to indicate tense of the verbs. Remember ASL uses root words. Topic is next to give the receiver the context of the message. The verb will give the action or reaction. This is followed by the adjectives and adverbs (as in Spanish, casa blanca——house white). The subject may begin the sentence and or end the sentence to clarify who was involved.

There is a device that the hospital should have in-house in areas such as the switchboard, emergency room, and social services for patient use. It is called a TTY (teletype) or TDD (telephone device for the deaf). It looks like a small typewriter with a phone modem above the keyboard. With a TTY a deaf person can use the telephone; messages are transmitted electronically through a series of signals. When you receive a TTY call, it will sound like a dead line or will have high pitched electronic beeps. Place the phone receiver in the modem and type in your greeting. To let the caller know you are ready for a response type GA (go ahead). You will notice the entire message is typed in all caps. There is no question mark, so you will use a letter, Q. To ask the person to hold, type PLS HD. All numbers will require use of the shift key. GA to SK (stop keying) means I'm finished is there anything you want to add. SK cues the receiver your message is complete and you are ready to hang up. If you have a typo you may go ahead or space over and try again or cross it out with x's. There is a backspace key to delete the errors from the LED screen. However if you have a printer attached all of the type will appear as it was entered mistakes and all. Use ER for emergency and DR for doctor. Keep questions short and to the point! No multiple choice questions; they are too difficult to be readily understood. If you forget and ask for instance, are you having nausea or cramps with vomiting and diarrhea. The answer you will most likely receive is yes. There is too much information to process and trying to get an accurate response could become frustrating for both you and the patient.

Some common phrases can be communicated as follows. For come in right away, type come now SK. Type when did you last see the doctor, as DR see when Q GA. What medication(s) are you taking for it should be typed as medicine what or medicine name. Lukewarm could best be described as hot cold mix. Chills as cold shake feel. Nausea as stomach complain. Asthma as breath hard or breath stuck and spotting as blood little bit.

Fine
'5' hand touches chest
and extends out

Lousy
'3' hand drops off
the nose

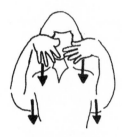

Sweat/Clammy
'4' hands down from
forehead, wiggle fingers
(also from armpits)

Feel/Sense/Emotion
'5' hand middle finger
strokes chest as it
moves up

Fragrance
Smell/Odor/Aroma
'5' hand moves up under
the nose, sniff

Office/Room/Box
'5' hands parallel to
each other flip in
at wrist

Home
closed hand thumb to
fingertips taps mouth,
then base of ear

Vomit
'5' hands pull up
from stomach & throw
out from body, open
mouth

Hospital/Clinic
'h' hand draws a
cross on the shoulder

Infect/Infection/Contagious
closed hand opens & spreads out over the top of the base hand

Break/Broken/Fracture
's' hands pull down and apart

Cast
'a' hand strikes top of other 'a' & then opens to spread over arm

Tired/Fatigue/Weary
'5' hands below ribs sag and fall open

Disease/Sick/Ill
'5' hands, middle fingers touch head and stomach

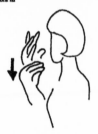

Sleep
'5' hand closes as head nods

Drip
'1' hand bent palm down points down from area of drip as in IV

Drool
'4' hand, index finger slides from mouth to chin

Drain/Discharge
'4' hand "flows" down from area of discharge

Contraction
'a' hands open &
close to "crawl"
across the stomach

Cramp/Contraction
's' hands twist pull
apart

Nausea
'claw' hand circles
the stomach, frown

Expectorate/Spit
'L' hand thumb & finger
touch "spews" from mouth
to 'l' hand

Swallow
'l' hand drawn from
mouth down throat

Chew
'a' hands knuckles
together, action
hand circles clockwise

Burp/Belch
's' hand changes to 'l'
as hand moves from chest
to throat

Attack
's' hand strikes &
recoils 'l' hand

Cut/Incision
'l' hand "cuts" across
back of the hand with
the index finger

Choke
grab the throat with
action hand

Breathe/Breath
'5' hands on chest move
in & out, inhale/exhale

Pant
'5' hands on chest
pat repeatedly

Weak/Faint
'5' hand rocks back &
forth in palm "weak
knees"

Strong/Power/Energy
'5' hand curves out
from shoulder to
elbow "like muscle"

Fall/Stumble/Trip
action person stands
& falls from palm

Bleed/Blood
'1' hand rubs lips &
changes to '5' to flow
across other hand wiggle
fingers

Wake/Awake
'g' hands at eyes open
to 'L' hands

Dizzy/Groggy
circle claw hand in
front of face, nod
head side to side

CHAPTER 11

FIRST AID

This last group of signs will round out your vocabulary in giving basic care to deaf and hearing impaired individuals.

When talking with the deaf patient be sure the light falls on your face. Never stand with your back to the window or the sun. Even the room lighting in the evening may reflect on the window glass and cause a glare for the lipreader. Be sure you have the patient's attention before you start talking. If the patient does not understand what you said or wrote, it is a good idea to rephrase it. Remember to be short and to the point.

Use words that will be more commonly understood by lay people. Be careful not to obscure your mouth. React to the deaf patient to let him know when you understand what he is saying. Please do not be guilty of **nodding appropriately**. It can give the patients a false sense of security or be taken as a brush off.

In American hearing culture we are very careful not to invade another's privacy, so we don't touch each other as a general rule. Deaf culture uses touching: to get someone's attention, to show support, to express empathy and acceptance. Deaf patients have been known to reach out and hug a nurse in the recovery room because they are more apprehensive or concerned about surgery than the hearing patient. This reaction may be the result of not having been properly prepared for surgery, not having good, clear communications from the beginning, not fully comprehending that the odds are in his favor, or a combination of these and other factors.

On occasion interpreters have been asked by the medical staff to sign papers for the deaf patient, to show that home care or some procedure was explained to the patient. This is not an interpreter's responsibility. If the patient refuses to sign the papers, the medical staff should handle it in the same way as when a hearing patient refuses to sign. An interpreter does not have the authority to sign any forms on the patient's behalf. The patient is in control of his own health care.

There is a sign you need to pay close attention to in the following illustrations. The sign for *clear/bright/light/obvious* can represent transparency as well as visual lighting. This sign applies to artificial light or the sun.

Bite
claw hand clamps down on side of '5' hand

Scrub/Wash
'a' hands knuckles together, action hand rubs back & forth

Clean/Nice
'5' hand wipes palm of the other hand

Dirty/Contaminate
'5' hand under the chin wiggle the fingers

Clear/Bright/Light
Obvious
'a' hands crossed open to '5' hands

Hazy/Subtle/Blurry/Fuzzy
'5' hands palms together move in alternating circles to obstruct the view

Compress
'5' hand wraps around area needing compress

Splint
'5' hands, action arm lays on top of base & then flips underneath

Sling
'1' hand draws a sling around arm

Dissolve/Melt/Fade/Dim
'5' hands slide closed

Exercise
's' hands move up
& down

Diaper
'3' hands stroke
diaper area

Burn/Fire
'5' hands palms in
move up & down fingers
wiggle

Bandage/Kind/Gentle
'5' hands fingers to-
gether action hand
circles the other

Bandaid
'h' hand slides across
back of other hand

Hearing Aid
'1' hand crooks index
over the ear

Improve
'5' hand bounces
up the arm

Deteriorate/Worsen
'5' hand bounces down
the arm

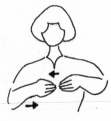

Itch/Scratch
claw hand scrathes the
arm or the itch

More
closed hands come
together

Calm/Peace/Quiet
'5' hands fingers to-
gether crossed slide
down & open

Rest/Relax
'5' hands folded in
rest across chest

Salt
'v' hand wiggles fingers
over 'h' hand

Insurance
shake 'i' hand

CHAPTER 12

THE INTERPRETER'S ROLE

In order to explain the interpreter's role it is important to define interpreter. An interpreter is someone who can take a source language, whether spoken or signed, and convert it into the target language so it will be readily understood by the deaf and hearing individuals involved. An interpreter should be able to communicate in a variety of different sign systems: Rochester Method, Seeing Essential English, Signing Exact English, Pidgin Sign English, American Sign Language, Minimal Language Skills and Mime/Gesture.

An interpreter must take a verbal message and convert it to the appropriate sign system without losing any of the meaning or context of the message. This procedure depends on a strong short-term memory to hold the message while the long-term memory matches the right deaf idioms and concepts to convert them to sign. An interpreter must be well rounded in knowledge in many areas; sometimes the interpreter's ability to interpret accurately depends on this general knowledge. An interpreter should be able to meet a deaf patient or client and assess his language skills or sign system and use that mode of communication for the entire time period involved. For example, if the deaf patient signs only in ASL it would be futile to converse with that patient in signed English. Although an interpreter works best for twenty to thirty minutes at a time, most situations last a minimum of two hours. For two hours the interpreter's brain is processing every word that is spoken or signed and converting it to the target language. Simultaneously the brain is reprocessing all of the information to correct or modify the interpretation to make it as accurate as possible. Consequently a good interpreter can and will think in sign. One of the most important tasks of the interpreter is to uphold the dignity of the deaf patient. Each person, hearing or deaf, has the right to be heard and to be in control of his or her health care. Interpreting takes years of practice and many hours of experience. The average time to become a competent interpreter is two to five years.

One sign language class does not an interpreter make, just as one semester in nursing or medical school will not qualify a person for a license.

Encourage your hospital administrators to use qualified professional interpreters in fulfilling their responsibilities under the law. In doing so you will have at the same time ensured the best possible communication with and treatment for the patient.

When working with an interpreter, talk directly to the patient, not to the interpreter. Look at the deaf person and talk as you normally would. The interpreter will respond as the voice of the deaf patient in the first person, not in the third. The interpreter is in effect the ears and voice of the patient, not of himself. If the patient is agitated and is fussing or cursing, the interpreter is obligated to voice the mood, tone, and comments or responses of the deaf patient without alteration. By the same token, whatever you say will be interpreted as well. If you do not want the deaf patient to eavesdrop on a conversation or to hear what is being said, do not expect the interpreter to be your censor. An interpreter is responsible for communicating everything spoken or signed, otherwise it appears the interpreter is withholding information or taking control of the situation. Interpreters are only there to ensure clear and precise communication. Interpreters are not privy to all information in a given situation. There should be no private conversations with the interpreter.

Professional interpreters may be found through contacting local chapters of the Registry of Interpreters for the Deaf (RID) or local organizations such as a Deaf Council. Texas hospitals may also contact Texas Commission for the Deaf (TCD) for state policies for interpreters and provision of interpreter services through TCD contractors.

Staff with limited sign knowledge can cause serious mistakes or misunderstanding. Interpreters are not qualified to start IV's or give injections. A beginning student of sign is not a qualified interpreter.

The Registry of Interpreters for the Deaf, in October of 1979, established an interpreters' code of ethics which govern our profession and protocol.

1. An interpreter/transliterator shall keep all assignment-related information strictly confidential.

Even if an interpreter knows all the information necessary to complete a patient's history, he is to refer all the questions to the deaf patient. Anything that is said is to remain with the parties involved. The patient may choose to share the experience and who interpreted. The interpreter, however, is not to divulge the name, sex, or age of the client. The time of the year, the location, and unnecessary specifics about a given situation are to remain confidential. The reason for confidentiality is that the deaf are so in tune with others in the deaf community, it is easy to guess who the client is with the least bit of information.

2. An interpreter/transliterator shall render the message faithfully, always conveying the content and spirit of the speaker, using language most readily understood by the person(s) whom he/she serves.

We cannot modify or edit any information. It must be signed or spoken exactly as it was intended. If the interpreter asks for clarification of a statement or word it is for the benefit of the patient and his understanding. Again, it would be necessary to address your answer directly to the patient. The latter part of this principle refers to using the choice of sign systems that the patient prefers or requires.

3. An interpreter/transliterator shall not counsel, advise, or interject personal opinions.

Were it not for the need of the deaf patient to have clear and precise communication, the interpreter would not be present. Therefore the interpreter is to refrain from any and all judgment calls or opinions.

4. An interpreter/transliterator shall accept assignments using discretion with regard to skill, setting, and the consumers involved.

Because facial expression plays such an important part in effective communication, it would be difficult to mask true feelings about a given set of circumstances. It is best for an interpreter to turn down an assignment in which there is a personality conflict or difficulty in understanding the client. It should also be noted that there are assignments which require such skill and expertise that a certified interpreter below that level must not accept.

5. An interpreter/transliterator shall request compensation for services in a professional and judicious manner.

6. An interpreter/transliterator shall function in a manner appropriate to the situation.

7. An interpreter/transliterator shall strive to further knowledge

and skills through participation in workshops, professional meetings, interaction with professional colleagues, and reading of current literature in the field.

8. An interpreter/transliterator, by virtue of membership in or certification by the RID, Inc., shall strive to maintain high professional standards in compliance with the code of ethics.

The interpreters' task is not easy but it can be rewarding when they are allowed to serve in their rightful capacity. Interpreters can lessen the time it takes to work with deaf patients. The interpreter can ensure that the deaf patient acts for himself with the dignity of free and unhindered communication. The interpreter will protect you and the patient as well as provide clear understanding for both the patient and the health care giver. We ask that you not be inhibited by the interpreter. The interpreter is there to serve and enhance your ability to give quality care in the patient's best interest. I must admit that we stand a little in awe of your skills and knowledge in the medical field. Interpreters deserve the same respect and opportunity to utilize our skills. Also, it is the law.

The Department of Health and Human Services (HHS) has issued regulations which apply Section 504 to hospitals and to other health care facilities. The HHS regulations stipulate that health care facilities which receive federal assistance must provide handicapped persons with services and benefits as effective as those provided to nonhandicapped persons. The facilities' responsibilities include the provision of auxiliary aids for effective communication between the patient and the medical team. These aids must include sign language interpreters, flash cards, lipreading (it is impossible to lipread through a surgical mask), written notes (remember English is a second language), supplementary hearing devices, charts, signs, or a combination of these. All of these must be available on a 24-hour basis for inpatient care and emergency services.

The following situations require interpreters according to HHS guidelines:

Securing the patient's medical history;
Securing informed consent and permission for treatment;
Explaining the diagnosis, treatment, and prognosis of an illness;
Communications in pre-op and recovery after surgery;
Explaining medication along with the dosage and possible side effects;

Explaining medical costs and insurance;

Explaining patient care upon release.

In the March/April 1985 issue of *The Voice*, P. J. Astin discussed the U.S. Supreme Court upholding a ruling against Baylor University Medical Center of Dallas, Texas. The Baylor Hospital receives Medicare and Medicaid coverage and was found in violation of Section 504 of the Rehabilitation Act of 1973. The hearing impaired patient was prevented from having the interpreter in for surgery preparation and recovery instructions. Although the patient had made prior arrangements with the doctor for an interpreter, when the surgery was moved up from 5:00 to 4:30 the interpreter was not contacted. The interpreter arrived after surgery had begun and was refused entry to the recovery room after surgery.

With more conscientious implementation of Section 504 of the Rehabilitation Act, health care professionals should be more aware and understanding of the needs of deaf people. We hope that one day the type of unfortunate incident described above will no longer occur. A hospital stay or medical procedure will be considerably less traumatic for the deaf when explanations are presented, via an interpreter, of what will be done. I hope that this book will contribute to that goal.

GLOSSARY

ASL—American Sign Language is the native manual language of the deaf in America. Syntax: Time, topic, verb, adjective, adverb, direct object, subject.

CSC—Comprehensive Skills Certificate awarded by the Registry of Interpreters for the Deaf.

Certification—A document awarded to interpreter/transliterators meeting the requirements of the board of evaluators for interpreters.

Classifier—A specific handshape used to designate a person or object which can be manipulated to show mannerisms, movement, etc.

Gallaudet University—First institution of higher education of the deaf which is located in Washington, D.C.

Gloss—The word or meaning attached to a sign as a point of reference for English speaking people.

ICTC—Interpreter Certificate/Transliterator Certificate awarded by the Registry of Interpreters for the Deaf.

Interpreter—A person able to fluently express and receive in ASL for communication between deaf and hearing individuals.

Minimal Language Skills—A basic language system composed of mime/gesture and may often include some home (family conceived) signs for manual communication.

Oral Deaf—A deaf person(s) relying on lipreading and basic speech skills for communication.

Placement—Using space to designate a person(s) or objects as they are distributed or to illustrate grammatical signals.

PSE—Pidgin Signed English a manual communication system using a combination of Signed English and ASL.

RID—Registry of Interpreters for the Deaf, a national organization created to standardize interpreting services, ethics and for skill evaluation.

Rochester Method—A manual communication system consisting of fingerspelling only.

Section 504—The portion of the Rehabilitation Act of 1973 guaranteeing equal access and the use of interpreters and various aids to increase the hearing impaired person's awareness and understanding in any situation requiring clear and precise communication.

Signed English—A manual language system using the English syntax

TCD—Texas Commission for the Deaf

TCD Level I—A basic level certificate awarded to interpreter/transliterators meeting the TCD Board of Evaluators of Interpreters (BEI) requirements for communicating at a slower speed.

TCD Level II—A mid-level certificate awarded to interpreter/transliterators meeting the TCD Board of Evaluators requirements for communicating at a normal speed.

TCD Level III—A comprehensive skill level qualifying the interpreter/transliterator for legal and medical situations. It is awarded by the TCD Board of Evaluators of Interpreters.

TCD Level IV—A higher comprehensive level awarded by the TCD Board of Evaluators.

TCD Level V—The highest comprehensive skill level awarded by the TCD Board of Evaluators.

TDD—Telephone Device for the Deaf, a keyboard with a modem for the phone receiver allowing the caller to transmit and receive typed messages on a LED screen and printer. Also called a TTY.

Transliterator—A person able to fluently express and receive in Signed English for communication between deaf and hearing individuals.

TTY—Teletype phone device, a keyboard with a modem for the phone receiver allowing the caller to transmit and receive typed messages on a LED screen and printer. Also called a TDD.

BIBLIOGRAPHY

Cochran, Cindy. *Signing With Cindy*. Gulf Publishing Co. Book Division, 1982.

Di Pietro, Loraine. *How Deaf People Communicate*. The Gallaudet University Press.

Garcia, W. Joseph. *Medical Sign Language*. Charles C. Thomas Publisher, 1983.

The Gallaudet Encyclopedia of Deaf People and Deafness. McGraw-Hill Publishers, Volumes 2 & 3. 1987.

Registry of Interpreters for the Deaf, Inc. Code of Ethics. 1979.

Sociology Department. *An Orientation to Deafness for Social Workers*. The Gallaudet University Press, 1975.

SIGN INDEX

77